Grateful

Today and Everyday

Wendy Ball Bridgeman

Grateful

Today and Everyday

Written By: Wendy Ball Bridgeman

ISBN: 978-1-7349862-7-3

This journal is dedicated to my
family and friends. I am
forever grateful for
your love and support.

This Journal Belongs To:

____

Date: ______________

Today, I am grateful for....

Date: ______________

Today, I am grateful for....

Date: ______________

Today, I am grateful for....

Date: ________________

Today, I am grateful for....

Date: ____________

Today, I am grateful for....

Date: ___________

Today, I am grateful for....

Date: ________________

Today, I am grateful for....

Date: ________________

Today, I am grateful for....

Date: ______________

Today, I am grateful for....

Date: ____________

Today, I am grateful for....

Date: ____________________

Today, I am grateful for....

Date: ________________

Today, I am grateful for....

Date: ___________

Today, I am grateful for....

Date: ____________

Today, I am grateful for....

Date: ____________

Today, I am grateful for....

Date: ____________

Today, I am grateful for....

Date: ___________

Today, I am grateful for....

Date: ______________

Today, I am grateful for....

Date: ______________

Today, I am grateful for....

Date: ____________

Today, I am grateful for....

Date: ______________

Today, I am grateful for....

Date: ______________

Today, I am grateful for....

Date: ___________

Today, I am grateful for....

Date: ______________

Today, I am grateful for....

Date: ______________

Today, I am grateful for....

Date: ______________

Today, I am grateful for....

Date: ______________

Today, I am grateful for....

Date: ________________

Today, I am grateful for....

Date: ________________

Today, I am grateful for....

Date: ________________

Today, I am grateful for....

Date: ______________

Today, I am grateful for....

Date: ________________

Today, I am grateful for....

Date: ____________

Today, I am grateful for....

Date: ______________

Today, I am grateful for....

Date: ____________

Today, I am grateful for....

Date: ______________

Today, I am grateful for....

Date: ______________

Today, I am grateful for....

Date: ____________

Today, I am grateful for....

Date: ______________

Today, I am grateful for....

Date: ________________

Today, I am grateful for....

Date: ____________

Today, I am grateful for….

Date: ________________

Today, I am grateful for....

Date: ______________

Today, I am grateful for....

Date: ___________________

Today, I am grateful for....

Date: ______________

Today, I am grateful for....

Date: ____________________

Today, I am grateful for....

Date: ______________

Today, I am grateful for....

Date: ____________

Today, I am grateful for....

Date: ______________

Today, I am grateful for....

Date: ___________________

Today, I am grateful for....

Date: ________________

Today, I am grateful for....

Date: ______________

Today, I am grateful for....

Date: ______________

Today, I am grateful for....

Date: ___________________

Today, I am grateful for....

Date: ______________

Today, I am grateful for....

Date: ________________

Today, I am grateful for....

Date: ____________

Today, I am grateful for....

Date: ___________________

Today, I am grateful for....

Date: ______________

Today, I am grateful for....

Date: ________________

Today, I am grateful for....

Date: ____________

Today, I am grateful for....

Date: ____________________

Today, I am grateful for....

Date: ____________

Today, I am grateful for....

Date: ___________________

Today, I am grateful for....

Date: ______________

Today, I am grateful for....

Date: ________________

Today, I am grateful for....

Date: ______________

Today, I am grateful for....

Date: ____________________

Today, I am grateful for....

Date: ____________

Today, I am grateful for....

Date: ______________________

Today, I am grateful for....

Date: ________________

Today, I am grateful for....

Date: ______________

Today, I am grateful for....

Date: ______________

Today, I am grateful for....

Date: ______________

Today, I am grateful for....

Date: _______________

Today, I am grateful for....

Date: ______________

Today, I am grateful for....

Date: ____________________

Today, I am grateful for....

Date: ______________

Today, I am grateful for....

Date: ____________

Today, I am grateful for....

Date: ________________

Today, I am grateful for....

Date: ____________

Today, I am grateful for....

Date: ______________

Today, I am grateful for....

Date: ______________

Today, I am grateful for....

Date: __________________

Today, I am grateful for....

Date: ______________

Today, I am grateful for....

Date: ________________

Today, I am grateful for....

Date: ______________

Today, I am grateful for....

Date: ____________

Today, I am grateful for....

Date: ______________

Today, I am grateful for....

Date: ______________

Today, I am grateful for....

Date: ______________

Today, I am grateful for....

Date: ______________

Today, I am grateful for....

Date: ________________

Today, I am grateful for....

Date: ______________

Today, I am grateful for....

Date: ______________

Today, I am grateful for....

Date: ______________

Today, I am grateful for....

Date: ____________

Today, I am grateful for....

Date: ______________

Today, I am grateful for....

Date: ______________

Today, I am grateful for....

Date: ________________

Today, I am grateful for....

Date: ____________

Today, I am grateful for....

Date: ________________

Today, I am grateful for....

Date: ____________

Today, I am grateful for....

Date: ______________

Today, I am grateful for....

Date: ______________

Today, I am grateful for....

Date: ___________________

Today, I am grateful for....

Date: ____________

Today, I am grateful for....

Date: ________________

Today, I am grateful for....

Date: ______________

Today, I am grateful for....

Date: ___________________

Today, I am grateful for....

Date: ______________

Today, I am grateful for....

Date: ________________

Today, I am grateful for....

Date: ______________

Today, I am grateful for....

Date: ________________

Today, I am grateful for....

Date: ____________

Today, I am grateful for....

Date: ___________________

Today, I am grateful for....

Date: ____________________

Today, I am grateful for....

Date: ______________

Today, I am grateful for....

Date: ________________

Today, I am grateful for....

Date: ___________

Today, I am grateful for....

Date: ______________

Today, I am grateful for....

Date: ______________

Today, I am grateful for....

Date: ____________

Today, I am grateful for....

Date: ________________

Today, I am grateful for....

Date: ____________

Today, I am grateful for....

Date: ____________

Today, I am grateful for....

Date: ____________

Today, I am grateful for....

Date: ________________

Today, I am grateful for....

Date: ____________

Today, I am grateful for....

Date: ________________

Today, I am grateful for....

Date: ______________

Today, I am grateful for....

Date: ________________

Today, I am grateful for....

Date: ____________

Today, I am grateful for....

Date: ________________

Today, I am grateful for....

Date: ___________________

Today, I am grateful for....

Date: ___________________

Today, I am grateful for....

Date: ______________

Today, I am grateful for....

Date: ____________________

Today, I am grateful for....

Date: ___________________

Today, I am grateful for....

Date: ______________

Today, I am grateful for....

Date: ____________________

Today, I am grateful for....

Date: ______________

Today, I am grateful for....

Date: ______________

Today, I am grateful for....

Date: ____________________

Today, I am grateful for....

Date: __________

Today, I am grateful for....

Date: ____________

Today, I am grateful for....

Date: ______________

Today, I am grateful for....

Date: ______________

Today, I am grateful for....

Date: ____________

Today, I am grateful for....

Date: ________________

Today, I am grateful for....

Date: ________________

Today, I am grateful for....

Date: ________________

Today, I am grateful for....

Date: ________________

Today, I am grateful for....

Date: ______________

Today, I am grateful for....

Date: ___________________

Today, I am grateful for....

Date: ____________________

Today, I am grateful for....

Date: ______________

Today, I am grateful for....

Date: ______________

Today, I am grateful for....

Date: ____________

Today, I am grateful for....

Date: ______________

Today, I am grateful for....

Date: ______________

Today, I am grateful for....

Date: ____________________

Today, I am grateful for....

Date: ____________

Today, I am grateful for....

Date: ________________

Today, I am grateful for....

Date: ______________

Today, I am grateful for....

Date: ____________

Today, I am grateful for....

Date: ________________

Today, I am grateful for....

Date: ________________

Today, I am grateful for....

Date: ______________

Today, I am grateful for....

Date: ____________________

Today, I am grateful for....

Date: ___________

Today, I am grateful for....

Date: ______________

Today, I am grateful for....

Date: ______________

Today, I am grateful for....

Date: ____________

Today, I am grateful for....

Date: ______________

Today, I am grateful for....

Date: ____________________

Today, I am grateful for....

Date: ____________

Today, I am grateful for....

Date: ____________

Today, I am grateful for....

Date: ____________

Today, I am grateful for....

Date: ________________

Today, I am grateful for....

Date: ______________

Today, I am grateful for....

Date: ______________

Today, I am grateful for....

Date: ____________

Today, I am grateful for....

Date: ________________

Today, I am grateful for....

Date: ______________

Today, I am grateful for....

Date: ____________

Today, I am grateful for....

Date: ____________

Today, I am grateful for....

Date: ______________

Today, I am grateful for....

Date: ___________________

Today, I am grateful for....

Date: ______________

Today, I am grateful for....

Date: ______________

Today, I am grateful for....

Date: ___________

Today, I am grateful for....

Date: ___________

Today, I am grateful for....

Date: ________________

Today, I am grateful for....

Date: ____________

Today, I am grateful for....

Date: ________________

Today, I am grateful for....

Date: ____________

Today, I am grateful for....

Date: ______________

Today, I am grateful for....

Date: ____________

Today, I am grateful for....

Date: ______________

Today, I am grateful for....

Date: ____________

Today, I am grateful for....

Date: ________________

Today, I am grateful for....

Date: ______________

Today, I am grateful for....

Date: ________________

Today, I am grateful for....

Date: ______________________

Today, I am grateful for....

Date: ____________

Today, I am grateful for....

Date: ______________

Today, I am grateful for....

Date: ______________

Today, I am grateful for....

CPSIA information can be obtained
at www.ICGtesting.com
Printed in the USA
LVHW052057121220
674005LV00003B/196

9 781734 986273